With love and best
wishes from Honeypot,

Tina x

THE SQUIRREL

Fiona C. Lunn

with illustrations by

Sara Westaway

Published by

LUNN LEARNING

www.lunnlearning.com

17 Water Eaton Road, Oxford OX2 7QQ

First published in Great Britain in 2019

Text copyright © Fiona C. Lunn 2019

Illustration copyright © Lunn Learning 2019

ISBN 978 1 913250 59 1

A CIP catalogue record for this book is available from the British Library.

Printed and bound in Great Britain by Remous Print

"All our papers are from farmed, replenished paper mills and trees grown specifically for paper production, all of which are fully recyclable and either PEFC or FSC accredited. Our production facility is as environmentally friendly as possible, all our waste paper is recycled along with all plastics and we use virtually no chemistry in the print process." Remous Print www.remous.com

This

book belongs to

. . . .

To Mr Nifty

My constant companion and my best friend

Photo by Neil Horne Photography www.eyeimaginephotography.com

"People need to see the tree in the acorn, the ship in the tree and the new world in the ship."   Anon

Pencil sketch by Sara Westaway

About the Author

Fiona C. Lunn MA(Oxon) is an exciting new talent on the children's books scene. She has been a private tutor in Oxford for over 35 years and is now writing novels to educate children about nature through fictional stories based on fact. The characters are animals in their natural environment and the stories give children an opportunity to learn about nature, wildlife and conservation. Fiona has three rescue dogs called Arnie, Benny and Cherry, and she was given Mr Nifty as a 'Nifty Fifty' birthday present. She loves to take them all for long walks in the park every day.

About the Illustrator

Sara Westaway is a professional artist, illustrator and designer based in North Dorset. She is inspired by nature and all types of animals and wildlife. She works predominantly in pencil which gives her work a soft nostalgic feel. Her work is very distinctive, and her aim is to produce uplifting pieces with a deep inner beauty.

Illustrations

1 "Hey! Whiskers!" Red called down to him.   16

2 "How am I doing what, Red?"   18

3 "What are you doing there, Red?"   20

4 Red leapt onto a huge, red mushroom.   26

5 He blinked big blinks and poked his head outside.   30

6 Red was starting to cry.   36

7 He lay there and fell fast asleep.   38

8 A pine marten was watching Red.   42

9 The pine marten reared-up like a bear.   44

10 "Yeah, bossss! Yeah!"   52

11 "No! No! It wasn't me!"   58

12 Whiskers stood to attention.   62

13 Stick was already there.   70

14 "We must wait for Her Ladyship."   74

15 Stick raised his paws and looked up to the sky.   82

16 "I have an idea!"   88

17 Red started munching on pine nuts.   96

18 The pine martens were watching Red.   102

19 This was a cunning plan!   108

20 "I'm going to show them my nuts!"   114

21 "I have brought delicious food to tempt them."   118

22 "Over here!"   120

23 "Here you are!" exclaimed Whiskers.   124

24 "Oh Red! Red! I thought you were dead!"   126

25 Red held-out his paw to shake PM's.   132

26 The other kit was a little bit shy.   138

27 "I call this one Cheeky Chops."   140

28 "Yeah! Let's shake on it!"   146

Contents

Foreword by Iolo Williams   13

Chapter 1   In the Forest   15

Chapter 2   The Invasion   29

Chapter 3   PM to the Rescue   41

Chapter 4   Red Spreads the News   55

Chapter 5   The Meeting of Minds   73

Chapter 6   Getting Ready   95

Chapter 7   Operation Grey-Away   111

Chapter 8   Happily Ever After?   123

INFORMATION   149

    What 'The Squirrel' teaches children   151

    The Red Squirrel   153

    The Pine Marten   161

    Charities   167

    Special Words   171

Foreword

I remember red squirrels being common around my home in Wales but when I return these days, I see nothing but greys. I have followed the success of various red squirrel projects with great interest and it is so heartening to see the reds striking back. Pine martens have come back to mid-Wales too and it is like welcoming back an old friend, really.

Thanks to the dedication of wildlife charities, our native squirrel and pine martens can once more be seen in British woodlands. With the work going from strength to strength, at least there is some hope for future generations.

'The Squirrel' is a lovely story about red squirrels and pine martens. I enjoyed reading it and I'm sure lots of children will love reading it too. So will their parents and grandparents because every adult is a child at heart, I think.

Iolo Williams Wildlife Expert and TV Presenter

Chapter 1

In the Forest

It was a lovely, warm, sunny day in autumn. Red the squirrel was leaping from tree to tree in the forest. He was finding pine cones in amongst the needles of the pine trees and squirrelling them away for the long, cold winter ahead.

Whenever he found one, he would check it to make sure there was nothing wrong with it, then he would bury it in the ground. Sometimes he'd find a really good one that was too good to resist, so he'd munch away on it and fill-up his tummy. This kept him big and strong. He needed lots of energy to do all this climbing and leaping and running and digging.

"Hey! Whiskers!" Red called down to him.

Red was a happy squirrel. He loved his life in the forest. He had lots of friends and everybody liked him. His best friend was Whiskers. He was called that because he had lots of very long whiskers and he twiddled them when he was thinking.

Red was up a tree when he saw Whiskers down on the ground below him. Whiskers was hunting for pine cones that had dropped onto the forest floor.

"Hey! Whiskers!" Red called down to him. "How are you doing?"

Whiskers looked-up with a startled look on his face. He twiddled his whiskers and replied, "How am I doing what, Red?"

Red had forgotten that Whiskers took everything literally, so he asked, "How are you, Whiskers?"

"How am I doing what, Red?"

THE SQUIRREL
Fiona C. Lunn

ISBN 978-1-913250-59-1

Available from
www.blackwells.co.uk

Teaching children about nature through stories.

www.lunnlearning.com

I'm stocking-up on
are you?"

love to stop and
time. Gotta dash!
he waved goodbye
etops.

t of pine cones so
nd and dug a hole
t, he dropped all
und and then he
arth.

ed and gold leaves
ground. These had
the forest such as
r Birch and Ash
erry.

leaves to cover
would find this
r. Then he stood

"What are you doing there, Red?"

still and twiddled the long, red hairs at the ends of his long, red ears. He was thinking.

"I hope I can remember where all my stores are," he thought. He took a long look around to try to remember this place. Then he heard a familiar posh voice.

"What are you doing there, Red?"

He looked up and could see her just above him. She was lying on a branch. It was Her Ladyship.

Whenever he saw her, his heart fluttered and his legs wobbled. He had no idea why. Perhaps it was her fabulous eyes that flashed as she looked at him. Perhaps it was her long, shiny claws that she tapped when she talked. Whatever it was, he got a funny feeling in his tummy and he went all nervous and shy.

"Oh… nothing…" he said nervously, as he turned and shuffled his paws to finish-off hiding his stash. He then quickly stood on top of it.

"Nothing? Really? I do not think so," she said. Then she slowly and gracefully climbed down the tree trunk and walked towards him.

He could feel his heart pounding. He could smell the sweet scent of her fur wafting in the breeze. She got closer and closer then stood beside him. He couldn't move. He was under her spell. He started to sway.

"You would not lie to me would you, Red?" she asked.

"No, m'lady."

"Are you sure?"

"Yes, m'lady."

"So what are you hiding under your paws?" She pointed down to the ground with one of her beautiful nails on a beautiful, delicate paw.

"Nothing, m'lady."

"Nothing?"

"Yes, m'lady."

She moved to be close to him. She was almost touching him. He felt her warm breath tickle his nose as she spoke.

"Stand aside, Red, and let me see," she commanded. He shuffled sideways. Nobody disobeyed Her Ladyship.

She looked where he'd been standing and there was nothing. All she could see was a pile of leaves. She didn't move any of them away. Her Ladyship never dug dirt or lifted leaves because that would damage her beautiful nails.

She looked straight at him. She fluttered her eyelashes and flashed her eyes as she stared into his. He couldn't breathe. He felt like he was going to faint.

"OK, Red. I believe you. There is nothing there so you were indeed doing 'nothing'. You really are a strange squirrel. Everyone is hurrying around storing food for the winter and you are here playing with a pile of leaves."

She looked at him with a puzzled look then she slowly - very slowly - turned to walk away. He relaxed and started breathing again.

Then, quick as a flash, she turned around and said, "I wonder if you will ever surprise me and do something to impress me, Red. I wonder…" And with that, she turned and leapt high in the air then bounced away on the forest floor. She was gone.

Red breathed a deep breath and sighed a huge sigh. "Phew! That was a close one!" he said with relief.

He twiddled the long, red hairs at the ends of his long, red ears and took one last look around to try to remember where this secret store was. "I'll never forget this place," he thought. "It's where I had my close encounter with Her Ladyship. I'll never forget that."

With a smile and a twinkle in his eyes, he bounced across the forest floor and leapt

Red leapt onto a huge, red mushroom.

onto a huge, red mushroom. There he sat, thinking about what had just happened. He laughed out loud and the other squirrels looked-up from what they were doing. They often saw Red smiling and often heard him laughing. Red was the 'happy chappy' of the forest and they all loved him for that.

There he sat until the light faded and it was time to go to bed. He thought he would sleep well that night…and he did.

Chapter 2

The Invasion

The days got shorter, the nights got longer and soon it was winter in the forest. All the squirrels were spending most of the time sleeping in their dens in the trunks of trees. They only ventured outside to quickly dig-up some food from their stores, then hurry back to snuggle-up and get warm again.

"Ahhh! This is the life!" said Red one morning, as he woke from a long slumber in his cosy bed of moss and leaves. He loved all the seasons: Spring was when he sprang into action and became a daddy; Summer was when he spent lots of time having fun with his friends; Autumn was when he fattened-up and stored food for the

He blinked big blinks and poked his head outside.

wintertime; Winter was when he slept and ate, and ate and slept, and slept and ate and so on…

He stretched his front legs and yawned a huge yawn. He blinked big blinks and poked his head outside. He looked-up through the pine trees and saw a blanket of grey cloud covering the sky. He sniffed quick sniffs and thought, "I can smell snow. I'd better get a wiggle on!" And with that, he had a good shake to fluff-up his fur and then he was off.

He climbed down the tree, then on the ground he scanned around to get his bearings. He twiddled the long, red hairs at the ends of his long, red ears and with a big smile he bounced along the forest floor to the stash of food he'd stored nearby.

When he got there, the leaves were gone. "Must have been blown away," he thought. He dug and dug, deeper and deeper but he didn't find anything.

"That's strange," he thought. "I'm sure I had a store here."

He twiddled his ear hairs and had a good think. Yes, he <u>had</u> stashed some food here. But where had it gone? "Somebody must've seen me burying it. Must be more careful next year," he thought, and off he went to get to his next store.

When he got there, the leaves were gone and the earth had been scratched away. There was only an empty hole where his food had been. Oh no! Not again! Red was a little bit upset. He thought that the other squirrels must have stolen his food.

He shrugged his shoulders and thought, "Fair's fair," because sometimes he took food that wasn't his if he found it when he was scratching for his own.

Off he bounced to the next store he'd made. Empty! And the next one. All gone! His tummy rumbled and he was feeling hungry. "Don't panic, Red." he said to himself. "THINK!"

He twiddled the long, red hairs at the ends of his long, red ears and then he remembered his encounter with Her Ladyship when he'd been stashing some pine cones. That store was deeper in the forest but he remembered exactly where it was. He climbed up a nearby trunk and jumped from tree to tree until he got to the one she'd been watching him from. Then he scurried down.

The ground was covered with scales from chewed pine cones and the earth around his store was all dug-away.

"NO!" he screamed. "NO!"

Red started to panic and he scratched and scratched at the ground. All he found was one half-chewed pine cone. All the rest had gone. He couldn't believe what he saw. His eyes filled with tears and he began to shiver. He was cold. Cold and hungry. Cold and hungry and scared.

He wanted to get home as fast as he could. He grabbed the half-chewed pine cone and ran up the tree. He jumped from branch to branch holding onto the little bit of pine cone as tightly as he could. He didn't stop. He got to his den and ran inside. He was safe.

As he nibbled and ate as quickly as he could, he started to think about the other squirrels stealing all his food. "Why would they do that? I thought they all liked me," he thought. Then he felt something wet drip onto his front paws. One drop. Then another. It wasn't rain leaking into his den. Red was starting to cry.

The days got even shorter and the nights got even longer. Snow fell and the forest was in the grip of a deep, cold winter.

Every day, Red searched and searched for his stored food. Every day, he found only a few morsels and had to return to his den cold and hungry. Some days he saw one or two of his friends, but he kept away from them because he was very upset that they could be so mean to him and steal all his food.

Red was starting to cry.

One day, when Red was desperately searching for food but hiding from the others, he watched them and noticed that their fur wasn't as red as it used to be. It was like his: shorter and dull and falling-out in places. They didn't move around like they used to. They were like him: weak and unsteady on their feet.

As he hid and watched, he noticed that some other strange squirrels were scurrying around. They were bigger and fatter and their hair was grey. The more he looked, the more of them he saw. The more he saw, the more he thought. The more he thought, the more he realised it was <u>these</u> squirrels that were stealing all the food. Every red squirrel was thin and starving but these grey ones were fat and healthy. Everywhere was swarming with big, fat, grey squirrels. The forest had been invaded!

He lay there and fell fast asleep.

Red hadn't eaten for days. He was very weak and very cold. He didn't have enough strength to climb up his tree to get back into his den. There was a log close-by so he crawled onto it and lay down to have a rest. He lay there and fell fast asleep.

Chapter 3

PM to the Rescue

Squirrels weren't the only things that lived in the forest. There were birds and beetles, ferns and fungi, flies and spiders, moths and midges, junipers and blueberries, and last but not least – pine martens.

As Red lay sleeping on the log, a pine marten had crept-up near to him and was watching him. Red didn't move. The pine marten wondered if he was dead. He crept a little bit closer and Red still didn't move. The pine marten sniffed at him and saw Red's chest slowly rise and fall as he breathed deeply in his sleep.

A pine marten was watching Red.

"So he's not dead then," the pine marten thought. "Not yet, anyway. Haha!" he giggled to himself, as he thought about how tasty red squirrels were. They were a real delicacy and a rare treat if they could be caught. They could leap high into the trees and they could run along fine branches, too delicate for a pine marten to follow. Pine martens are too big for that – they're the size of a cat!

"Yummy, yummy, yummy. Food for my tummy!" the pine marten thought, as he slobbered saliva onto Red's scruffy fur.

Red's tatty fur stuck to his skin and the pine marten could see how thin and scrawny he was. "Mmm… All bone and no meat. He won't be tasty at all," he thought. "Just like them other ones I ate. Crunch, crunch, crunch and no juicy bits. Had to spit 'em out in the end."

The pine marten reared-up like a bear.

He took a step backwards and a twig snapped with a loud crack as he stood on it. "Oops!" he thought. "It don't matter. Them squirrels don't eat pine martens just pine nuts. Haha!"

"I'm so hungry I could eat a horse…" Red muttered in his sleep.

"A horse?!" the pine marten cried out loud. "Yikes! I'm off!"

This woke Red with a start. He opened his eyes and saw two big, brown eyes staring back at him. "Ahhh!" Red cried-out with fright. "Who are you?" he shouted, trying to disguise his fear.

The pine marten reared-up like a bear and Red let-out a squeal. He thought he was going to die of starvation. He didn't think he was going to be eaten by a bear!

"I'm a pine marten. PM's the name. And you are…?"

"Red. I'm a red squirrel but I'm not very red any more. I'm not very well, you see." Red answered nervously.

"Good job I didn't eat yer, then. Don't want to get the lurgy from yer."

That gave Red an idea. "I'm all skin and bone," Red continued. "I wouldn't be tasty and I might give you worms."

"Worms?"

"Yes. Wiggly little parasites that live inside you and eat you up from inside out," Red continued.

"Yuk! That's disgustin'! An' I ate one of you lot earlier," moaned PM as he started to feel sick.

Red heard alarm bells ringing in his ears and his mummy's voice came back in a flash: "If you ever see one of those weasel-like creatures with dark brown fur and a creamy-white bib, run for your life! Run for your life! Run for your life!"

Her warning repeated over and over in his mind. But Red couldn't run. He could barely walk. This was it. He slumped back on the log and he thought he was going to be eaten alive. At that moment, he heard PM being sick.

"Are you OK?" Red asked in his usual caring way.

"I feel as sick as a dog, Red. I don't think I'll ever eat another one of you lot ever again."

PM slumped on the log beside Red. There they sat, prey and predator side-by-side, both of them looking rather sorry for themselves.

All was quiet. No rustling on the ground, no bird calls in the air. Everything was silent. Then Red's tummy made a huge rumbling sound.

"Cripes! You sound 'ungry, Red."

"I am," Red whimpered.

"Why's that, then?"

"The grey squirrels have stolen all my food and I can't find any and I'm starving."

"Fancy some nuts or seeds or fruit or mushrooms or…"

"Yes!" cried Red.

"Well! Follow me, Red! I know where them grey squirrels 'ave 'idden it all. Come on. Let's get some food inside yer."

One of the strangest sights that the other animals had ever seen was when they watched a red squirrel follow a pine marten on a treat trail along the forest floor. Normally, it would be the other way round and the pine marten would be following the squirrel, chasing it up a tree. But not today...

When PM got back home, his dutiful servant, One Fang, was waiting for him. He lost one of his fangs when he escaped from a fox trap. And he lost his left eye too.

"Cor, you're late. What happened to you, bossss?" asked One Fang with a rough, husky voice.

"I got talkin' to a red squirrel," PM replied with a glint in his eye.

"Talkin'? Not eatin'? You going soft, bossss?"

"What did yer say?"

"Nothing, bossss. Nothing." One Fang knew not to make his boss cross. "What did you talk about, bossss?"

"I got friendly-like with one of 'em called Red. I think I know how to get the lot of 'em - the greys <u>and</u> the reds."

"The greys <u>and</u> the reds, bossss? The greys are easy cos they're big an' fat an' can't climb trees as high. But the reds, bossss? We can get the reds as well? Blimey!"

"That's right. Listen-up. I showed Red where the greys stashed their food. I said we'd help the reds find more to get 'em through the winter."

"Why, bossss?"

"That way they get big and strong and we get 'em on our side. Right?"

"Right, bossss."

"An' I gave Red an idea of how to chase the greys away so the reds get back their forest."

"Why, bossss?"

"That way we all live happily ever after. Right?"

"Right, bossss."

"Wrong! Hahaha…"

"Wrong, bossss?"

"Yeah, bossss! Yeah!"

PM grinned a naughty grin and said,
"Yeah… Haha! We fatten 'em up and then
we eat 'em up!"

One Fang punched the air with his fist
and shouted with glee, "Yeah, bossss! Yeah!"

PM and One Fang pranced around,
swishing their tails as they chanted, "Fatten
'em up then eat 'em up! Fatten 'em up then
eat 'em up!"

They looked straight at each other with
sneers of delight. PM was good at making
plans and this one was a cunning one. A
very cunning one indeed.

Chapter 4

Red Spreads the News

Red's tummy was full, really full, and as he waddled through the forest he let-out a huge burp.

"Buuurrrppp! Ah, that feels better." He rubbed his full tummy and thought, "This must be what the girl-squirrels feel like when they're expecting babies. I'm glad I'm a boy-squirrel and I don't have to lug a lump like this around for weeks. I'll never make fun of them again when they're expecting!"

He waddled on, chattering to himself, burping-away and doing some botty-burps too.

"Who's there?" came a weak and timid voice from a nearby tree trunk.

"It's me," replied Red, looking around to see where the voice was coming from.

"Who's me?" asked the voice.

Red twiddled his ears and a few hairs dropped out. "Who's me?" he thought. He didn't know who it was and he decided it must be some sort of game.

"I don't know who you are," he said with a giggle. Red was in a very good mood now that he had a very full tummy.

"No, I meant who are <u>you</u>?" said the faint voice.

"I'm Red."

"Red? Oh Red…" and slowly a head appeared at a hole in the tree trunk next to where Red was standing. It was Whiskers.

"Hello Whiskers!" exclaimed Red. "How are you? I haven't seen you in ages."

Then Red noticed something strange. Whiskers hadn't got his magnificent moustache any more. There were just one or two whiskers where it used to be.

"I'm not very well," replied Whiskers. "I'm very hungry. All my food's been stolen." Then Whiskers noticed Red's huge, bulging tummy. "Did <u>you</u> steal all my food?" he asked.

"No! No! It wasn't me!" exclaimed Red.

Red told Whiskers all about his food being stolen too. He told him that grey squirrels had invaded the forest and that <u>they</u> were the ones stealing all the food. He described how a pine marten had come to his rescue and that it had shown him where the grey squirrels had stored all the food.

"No! No! It wasn't me!"

As Red told his story, Whiskers felt a little bit stronger and when Red had finished, he crawled out of his den and staggered to the ground where Red was standing.

"So what's the plan?" Whiskers asked.

"Plan?" said Red. "There isn't a plan. Just eat the food, I guess."

"Well that's OK for now," said Whiskers, "but then what?"

Red twiddled his ears and a few more hairs dropped-out. He looked at them in his scrawny claws and realised that just eating the food wasn't going to solve the big problem of the grey squirrels living in the forest.

"Let's go see Stick. He'll know what to do," said Red.

"Good idea," said Whiskers. "I knew you'd have a plan!"

So they set-off to see Stick. On the way, Red showed Whiskers some of the places where PM had said the grey squirrels were storing food. Whiskers eagerly munched on some of the pine cones they found and he began to feel much better already.

When they got to Stick's den, they peered into the hole in the ground. Stick was a wise red squirrel. He was too old to climb trees so his den was deep down in the ground at the base of the biggest pine tree in the forest.

"Stick!" they both shouted down the hole. "Stick!" they called again. Silence.

"He must be sleeping," said Red. "You stay here and I'll crawl down and find him."

"You can't do that!" Whiskers said nervously. "That's not allowed!" Whiskers was very well-mannered and he knew it wasn't polite to just barge into somebody's home.

"But it's an emergency," said Red. "We need to pick Stick's brain."

"What? That's disgusting!"

"I don't mean we actually pick at his brain," Red explained. He'd forgotten that Whiskers took everything literally. "I mean we need to ask Stick what we should do."

"Oh, that's OK. Why didn't you say that?"

"Erm… well… it's…" Red couldn't explain.

Whiskers stood to attention.

"I'll stay here and you crawl down and find him," said Whiskers, as if it was his idea. "I'll call if anyone's coming."

"OK," Red nodded.

Whiskers stood to attention on the look-out at the entrance to Stick's den and Red entered the hole.

Red crawled slowly and carefully along the narrow tunnel. Down and down he crawled. There was a little bit of light entering from the hole where Whiskers was standing, but as he crawled further the light faded and soon Red was in total darkness.

"Stick. Are you there, Stick?" he whispered.

Then he thought, "Why am I whispering? I'm trying to wake him up. I should be shouting."

"STICK!" he shouted. "STICK!"

He stopped and listened. He couldn't hear anything. Then he felt something crawling on his neck.

"Yuk! What's that?" he said out loud and flicked something out of his fur. "Creepy-crawlies give me the creeps," he muttered, as he started to crawl forwards again even deeper into the tunnel.

On and on he went. Then he had a thought. What if this was the wrong tunnel? What if this wasn't leading to Stick's den? What if he was crawling down into a rabbit warren, or into a badger sett, or into a fox's den?

He started to panic and tried to turn round but the tunnel was too narrow. He shrieked and shrieked and made such a noise that he could hear it echoing around. He thought it was coming from another animal and it made him shriek even louder. That was when he heard Stick's impressive voice.

"Who on Earth is making that racket? Shut up and get out of my den. Get out or I'll whack you with this stick. Be gone, I say!"

Red crawled forwards into the inner chamber of the den. "Oh Stick! It's me. It's Red," he sighed in relief.

"Red? Why are you down here?" Stick's voice was calm and sounded concerned.

Red told Stick what he'd told Whiskers. He told him that all his food had been stolen and that grey squirrels had invaded the forest and were stealing all the food. He described how a pine marten had come to his rescue and that the pine marten had shown him where the grey squirrels had stored all the food. He added that all the red squirrels were thin and not very well and that Whiskers had lost all but a few of his wonderful whiskers.

As Red told his story, Stick was completely silent. When he'd finished, he waited to hear Stick's response, but Stick said nothing. Everything was silent. It was a bit spooky.

"Stick? Are you still there, Stick?" Red asked.

"Yes." There was silence again.

"Did you hear what I said, Stick?"

"Yes of course I did. I may be old and doddery but I'm not deaf. Not yet anyway," said Stick, a little bit irritated.

Red realised he should keep quiet. Stick was thinking, and when Stick was thinking he needed it to be quiet.

After what seemed like forever, Stick took a deep breath and said, "I have a plan. Go get Whiskers and send a message to Her Ladyship to ask if she would kindly meet us all by The Stump. I'll see you there. Hurry! There's no time to waste."

"Yes, Stick! Will do!" said Red.

He turned and scampered up the tunnel as fast as he could. He wasn't as fit as he used to be and he often had to stop to catch his breath. He could see the light at the end of the tunnel. He kept going and soon he was out.

Whiskers was still there and still standing to attention. When he saw Red he breathed a huge sigh of relief.

"Crikey! You were gone a long time, Red. I nearly came in after you but I didn't want to leave my post."

"You did the right thing, Whiskers," said Red. "Stick's got a plan. We've got to get a message to Her Ladyship and we must all meet him by The Stump as quickly as we can."

"I'm on it!" said Whiskers, and he started to whistle a strange tune.

"What's that?" asked Red.

"It's my call to Her Ladyship. We have a special call to each other."

"Oh…" said Red, a little bit sad that Whiskers had a special friendship with Her Ladyship but that he didn't.

Whiskers could see that Red looked a bit sad. "What's the matter?" he asked.

"Nothing," Red said as he looked down and shrugged his shoulders. Then he put on a brave face and continued. "Nothing. I'm just a little bit tired that's all. Come on! Let's get to The Stump!"

They scurried across the forest floor. They weren't well enough to climb the trees and leap from branch to branch like they normally would. They rushed across the floor and were panting heavily when they got to The Stump.

Stick was already there. They were shocked by how frail he looked. He seemed much older and thinner than when they last saw him and now he had some grey hairs and a few bald patches too. He was standing calmly and using his 'stagger stick' to steady himself.

Stick was already there.

"How did you get here so quickly?" panted Red, as he and Whiskers ran to The Stump. "We came as fast as we could and you're not even out of breath."

"Secret passages!" explained Stick. "The forest floor is full of dark, secret passages. There's a huge network of old burrows from long ago and I know them all well. When you're as old as me, you'll know them too, but until then they're mine. My shortcuts to here, there and everywhere." He smiled a knowing smile and had a twinkle in his little eyes that he'd screwed-up tight in the light.

Red was fascinated. He wanted to grow old and wise like Stick and he wanted to find out about all the secret passages. He took a long look at Stick and he could see how old and frail he was. Red decided he'd visit Stick much more from now on.

Chapter 5

The Meeting of Minds

Red, Whiskers and Stick were standing around The Stump. "So what's the plan?" asked Whiskers, excited by it all.

Stick slowly raised a front paw and said, "We must wait. We must wait for Her Ladyship."

As he lowered his paw to clutch onto the tree stump again, there was a rustling sound behind them. They all turned and she was standing there before them. They all stared.

Was this Her Ladyship? Was it really her? Where was her sleek and shiny fur coat? Where were her beautiful nails?

"We must wa

er Ladyship."

"Greetings everyone," she spoke softly. It was the same posh voice. They were the same flashing eyes. Yes, it was Her Ladyship, but she looked so different.

"It is rude to stare," she announced, as she adjusted a headband she had made from ivy. She took her place at The Stump and then they all turned to look at Stick.

"Are you all listening carefully?" Stick asked.

They all nodded and stood still in silence. Stick knew he had their attention and so he raised his head high and started to speak in a loud, clear voice.

"This meeting is to discuss how we're going to get our forest back. We are here to discuss how we're going to get rid of those grey squirrels."

Stick was standing upright. His eyes were screwed-up tightly and he had a powerful look about him.

Everyone respected Stick. He was old and wise and always right. They all listened carefully, hoping that Stick would tell them exactly what they were going to do.

"We need a plan. We need a battleplan," Stick announced.

"Hear hear!" the others all said together. Stick was encouraged by their positive attitude and so he continued.

"I am your General. I do all the general planning. Red is your Colonel. Colonel Red shall be in charge during the operation. Everyone shall obey his commands without question."

Her Ladyship slowly turned her head to look straight at Red. He tried not to notice but he felt her eyes flash at him. He went hot and his tummy fluttered. She turned back and continued listening to Stick.

"Major Whiskers shall be in charge of signals," Stick continued. "He is an expert whistler. Everyone must listen for his calls and follow his signals without question."

Whiskers twiddled the few remaining whiskers he had and he looked very pleased. He stood to attention and saluted General Stick and then saluted Colonel Red.

Stick gave a quick nod to Whiskers then continued. "I shall now describe what…"

"Excuse me, General Stick," interrupted Her Ladyship.

"Yes ma'am."

"What shall my role be in this operation?"

"Well, ma'am. I didn't think…"

"You did not think?" she interrupted. "Tut, tut, General Stick. You think of everything." She paused to give him time to think.

After a short while, he gave a little cough to clear his throat and then said, "I beg your pardon, ma'am. You are Secretary of State."

"A secretary? You consider <u>me</u> to be a secretary?"

"No ma'am."

"Then I shall have a different role to that. I request you think of a better one with a better title. In the meantime, let us get down to business. Titles are merely that – titles. It is what one <u>does</u> that matters, so what are we going to <u>do</u>, General Stick?"

Stick cleared his throat again and he continued. "We are all starving and we are all suffering from ill health. Why? Because our food has been stolen. Why? Because grey squirrels are eating it. Why? Because they have invaded our forest in vast numbers. Is this correct, Colonel Red?"

Red nodded.

"Pardon? I didn't hear you, Colonel Red."

"Sir, yes sir!" he answered, standing to attention.

Stick was pleased and so he continued.

"We must chase the grey squirrels away so that we can return to the way things were before they invaded."

Stick raised his paws and looked up to the sky with a fierce look on his face. "We need to live in <u>our</u> forest and eat <u>our</u> food and we all need to live happily ever after!" Stick seemed angry - very angry indeed.

After a few deep breaths, Stick calmed-down and slowly looked at Red, then Whiskers, then Her Ladyship. He cleared his throat and said, "That is <u>what</u> needs to be done. Now we must discuss <u>how</u> it will be done. I open the floor for discussion."

Whiskers shrieked and jumped up onto the tree stump.

"What on earth is wrong with you, Major Whiskers?" Stick demanded.

Stick raised his paws and looked up to the sky.

"You're opening-up the floor!" Whiskers cried. "I don't want to fall into it!"

"No, no, no," said Red, with a calm voice as he looked up at Whiskers trembling on The Stump. "General Stick meant that we can all talk freely about our ideas of how to chase the grey squirrels away."

"Oh. Why didn't he say that?" asked Whiskers, with a puzzled look on his face.

"Erm… well… it's…" Red couldn't explain.

Her Ladyship looked-up at Whiskers and smiled a warm and gentle smile. Then she spoke to Whiskers in a way that nobody else had ever heard before.

"I can explain it to you later, Whiskers dear, when this wretched battle is over and we are warm and well and we can get on with our lives. Come down and stand by me, my dear. You are quite safe." Whiskers bowed graciously and clambered down off the tree stump.

He stood beside her. She placed her paw on his paw and gave it a gentle squeeze to reassure him that all was well. He breathed a big sigh of relief.

"You may continue, General Stick," she commanded.

"Thank you, ma'am. As I said, I open the floor for discussion." There was silence. Nobody said a word. "Well? Who has an idea?"

The silence continued. Red shuffled his paws awkwardly.

"Yes, Colonel Red? You have an idea?"

"Sir, I was just shuffling my paws, sir."

The silence continued. Then Whiskers raised his front paw. Stick looked pleased.

"At last somebody is brave enough to get the ball rolling."

"Sir, I haven't got a ball. I just want to ask…" and then Whiskers lost his courage to ask his question.

"Well? What is it? We haven't got all day," Stick snapped.

"I just wanted to ask if I could leave the meeting."

"Why? It's only just started."

"I need to… to go to… to go to the toilet," Whiskers stammered and looked as if he was about to cry.

"What a splendid idea, Whiskers!" said Her Ladyship. "I think we could all do with a toilet break. All those in favour raise your paw." Whiskers immediately raised his paw, followed by Her Ladyship, followed by Red.

They all looked at Stick who seemed quite irritated. "Oh, very well. Be quick. That's an order! I'll count down from 20 and if you're not all back by the time I finish, there will be serious consequences. 20... 19... 18..."

Whiskers scurried-away. Red followed and as he watched Whiskers disappear into the distance, he got an idea. He twiddled the few hairs he had left on the ends of his ears and had a quick think, then he returned to The Stump with a big smile on his face.

"8... 7... 6..."

Whiskers rushed back and quickly stood to attention as Stick said, "3… 2… 1… Attention!"

Stick glared at Whiskers and after a long, hard look he decided to be less strict and said, "Alright, Major Whiskers. You may stand at ease."

Red raised his front paw. Stick frowned and exclaimed, "Now what? Really, this is becoming intolerable."

"Sir, permission to speak, sir," said Red.

"Permission granted," replied Stick.

Red cleared his throat and said, "I have an idea!"

Her Ladyship raised an eyebrow and slowly turned her head. She looked straight at him. Red's heart was pounding and his tummy fluttered but he stayed calm and said one word.

"I have an idea!"

"Temptation".

Her Ladyship's eyes twinkled and she gave him a big smile and winked at him.

Red felt he was about to faint but he took a deep breath and said, "We need to tempt the greys away with nuts and make them go to a place where the pinc martens will chase them out of the forest and keep them out for ever."

There was a stunned silence. Then everybody spoke at once, asking Red lots of questions. Where would they get the nuts from? What place would they go to? Why would the pine martens help? Who would be brave enough to tempt the greys away? When would this happen? How would the pine martens keep the greys out of the forest?

Red didn't know who to answer first but he did know the answers to all the questions. Everyone became very excited and had lots of ideas.

Stick paced around using his 'stagger stick' to steady himself. He listened to all the ideas, he listened to all the questions and he listened to all of Red's answers. When he'd heard enough, he decided to bring the meeting back to order.

Stick stood by The Stump, raised his 'stagger stick' high in the air and called-out in a booming voice, "ORDER!"

They all turned to look at Stick then returned to their places at The Stump and were silent as he began to speak.

"I have listened to all your questions. I have listened to all of Colonel Red's answers. I have heard all your ideas. I am very impressed."

He paused and looked straight at Red then turned to address Her Ladyship.

"Your Ladyship. You asked, 'Who would be brave enough to tempt the greys away?' I know exactly who that is. It is Colonel Red. I propose that Colonel Red is not only in charge of the operation but he also leads it."

Everyone looked at Red. He didn't move. He was frozen by fear. Stick continued, "All those in favour of Colonel Red leading the operation say 'Aye' and those against say 'Nay'."

Everyone said 'Aye'. Nobody said 'Nay'.

"The vote is unanimous," proclaimed Stick. "Colonel Red leads the operation."

Whiskers clapped his paws and cheered with delight.

Stick continued, "I shall create the battleplan based on all of your superb ideas. The operation shall have the codename 'Operation Grey-Away'. This meeting is now over."

He tapped his stick against The Stump and everyone began to walk away. Everyone except Red.

Red stood motionless as he stared into the distance. "What have I done?" he asked himself. "Why did they all vote 'Aye' for me to be the leader?"

Red began to tremble. Her Ladyship's whisper in his ear broke his trance.

"I did wonder if you would ever surprise me and do something to impress me, Red," she said softly.

He turned to look at her. His heart did its usual flutter but this time he was able to look at her without feeling faint. She was so close that he could smell the sweet scent of her fur and he could feel her warm breath on his face.

She continued, "I think this might be it, Red. I am impressed that it will be <u>you</u> who will be leading the operation."

She smiled and stroked her tail with her paws then she turned to leave. Quick as a flash, she turned back and said, "Yes! I am <u>very</u> impressed!"

She winked at him, then did her usual leap in the air and bounced away on the forest floor. She was gone.

Red stood there for some time thinking about everything that had happened. Was he brave enough to be the leader? Would he do a good job? He really didn't know.

"There's only one way to find out," he said out loud. Red puffed-out his chest and said, "I am Colonel Red and I am in charge!"

He liked the sound of that. He smiled his huge smile but then he felt very tired.

"I'd better go to bed," he thought. So he went back to his den for some supper and a good night's sleep.

Chapter 6

Getting Ready

Red woke-up the following morning and didn't know if he'd been dreaming or if it had actually happened. Was he really going to be in charge? Was he really going to lead the operation? Then he remembered the meeting and he remembered the vote. Yes he <u>was</u> going to be the leader.

"I'd better get started," he thought.

He stretched his front legs and yawned a huge yawn. He blinked big blinks and jumped out of bed. He stood to attention, puffed-out his chest and said out loud with confidence, "I am Colonel Red and I am in charge!"

Red started munching on pine nuts.

He had a good shake to try to fluff-up
his thin fur and then he climbed down from
his den.

First, he needed some breakfast.
"Breakfast is the most important meal of the
day," his mummy had said to him every
morning. He was skinny and his hair was
falling out but all that would change soon
because PM had shown him where the grey
squirrels had stashed all the food.

He went to the nearest store and
started munching on pine nuts. As he
nibbled on his breakfast, he realised that all
the other red squirrels needed breakfast too.
They all needed to know where the greys
had stashed the food.

He twiddled the few remaining hairs on
his ears and thought about how to get
everybody fit and healthy again. He started
to make a plan.

When he'd eaten as much as he could eat, Red set-off to see Whiskers. He was going to tell him where all the food was and ask him to whistle signals to all the red squirrels around the forest so that they knew too.

On the way, he noticed that every red squirrel that saw him stood to attention and saluted him. "That's odd," he thought. He waved back and carried-on to see Whiskers.

A little while later, he got to where Whiskers lived and instantly Whiskers climbed down the tree and marched towards him. He saluted Red and said, "Good morning, Colonel."

"Erm… Good morning, Whiskers."

"Major Whiskers at your service, sir," he replied, standing to attention and saluting him.

"Thank you, Whiskers, but…erm… I don't think we need to do all this military stuff until it's time for 'Operation Grey-Away'."

Whiskers slowly dropped his paw and slowly stopped standing to attention. He was disappointed. He enjoyed being Major Whiskers.

Red could see he was sad, so he quickly started telling him where the food stores were and asked him to whistle to all the other red squirrels to let them know too. Instantly, Whiskers cheered-up and started whistling away!

"Now then, Whiskers," said Red. "You need to do this every morning like the wake-up trumpet call in the army."

"Great!" said Whiskers. "I can do that!"

"This is important so that we all have good breakfasts and eat well every day throughout the winter."

"Great!" said Whiskers. "We can do that!"

"Then we'll be able to do 'Operation Grey-Away' when we're all big and strong and the greys are hungry and needing food."

"Great!" said Whiskers. "We'll get rid of the greys!" he cried, and he jumped around and punched the air with his paws.

"Yes we will, Whiskers!" Red raised a front paw and said, "High Paws!" Whiskers raised his front paw and they slapped their paws together. Red waved goodbye and set-off to do the next part of his plan. He was going to see PM.

The part of the forest where the pine martens lived was strictly 'Out of Bounds' as far as the squirrels were concerned. None of them ever ventured into that dark and damp place.

"You'll get eaten alive!" his mummy had told him. "Don't ever go there!" she had said. But Red was sure that PM wasn't like that. PM had helped him find food. PM had given him the idea of how to chase the greys away. PM seemed nice and friendly. Surely PM wouldn't eat him alive? Surely not.

As he got near to where the pine martens lived, he felt he was being watched. He stopped and looked around but he couldn't see anybody. He carried-on walking and he thought he saw dark shadows moving in the trees. He stopped. He looked-up but there was nobody there. Or so he thought…

The pine martens were watching Red.

The pine martens were watching Red. PM had told them all about the cunning plan to fatten-up the red squirrels then eat them up. They could see that Red was really skinny so not a tasty meal at all - not yet anyway. They let him get deeper and deeper into their part of the forest and signalled to PM that he was approaching.

"How are yer doin' there, Red?" a voice asked from in the trees.

Red stood motionless as if he was frozen to the spot. "Who...who...who's the...the...there?" Red asked with a quivering voice.

"It's me! PM! How's things with yer?" called PM, and he ran down the tree next to where Red was standing.

"Oh, PM. It's you!"

"Haha! Yeah, it's me. Are yer eatin' all the food I showed yer? Got all the others eatin' it too?"

"Oooh yes, PM. Thank you so much for being so kind. We're all eating well and we'll soon be big and strong. We'll be well enough to chase the greys away by springtime like you said."

"That's good news, Red. Happy to help! Why are yer here?"

"Well it's to chat about your idea and make a plan," Red replied.

"Cool! Let's get down to it." PM let out a loud squeal and instantly his dutiful servant, One Fang, appeared and stood by his side.

Red stared at him. He saw the empty socket where his left eye used to be. He saw a chunk had been torn out of his left ear. He saw the long scar running down from his ear to his mouth and the gap where a fang should be. Red realised he must have been in terrible pain when he got these injuries. Instantly, Red felt sorry for him.

"You called, bossss?" said One Fang, with his rough, husky voice.

"Yeah. I want you two to meet. Red, this is One Fang. One Fang, this is Red." They both nodded to each other. "Right. Let's get down to it. Here's the plan."

The three of them huddled together and PM described how the red squirrels and the pine martens could chase the greys away.

"First, yer need to get the greys into the cleared section of the forest. Maybe leave a few nuts and acorns lyin' around. Have a trail of food so them greys go all the way down the clearing. At the end, we'll be waitin'. When we see 'em, we'll leap-out and chase 'em. They'll be so frightened, they'll run far away from the forest an' they'll never come back!"

"Oh PM, that sounds wonderful! Your plan sounds perfect. We'll do exactly as you say! Thank you so much," Red exclaimed with a huge smile.

Red left with a happy skip and jump in his walk. When he was out of sight, One Fang turned to PM with a puzzled look on his face.

"So we don't get to eat them greys, bossss?" he asked.

"Yeah."

"Yeah we don't or yeah we do, bossss?"

"Yeah we do."

"How come, bossss? You said we'll chase 'em away."

"I know I did. That was to fool Red and make him keep his side of the bargain. We're gonna chase 'em into a trap."

"A trap, bossss?"

"Yeah! We'll trap 'em and eat 'em then go back for the reds!"

Their mouths started to dribble. They looked straight at each other with sneers of delight.

This was a cunning plan!

This was a cunning plan!

Red went to see Stick straight away and he told him all about the plan.

"Well done, Red," exclaimed Stick. "You have thought-up a masterplan. It's far better than the one I was working-on. Well done!"

Red didn't have the courage to admit it was actually one of the pine martens who had thought it up.

"And what about food? Where are we going to get food?" asked Stick.

"I know where the greys have stashed it!" replied Red.

"Oh well done, Red. Well done. I knew you'd be the right one to be in charge. Well done!"

Red smiled but it was a fake smile. He felt guilty about taking credit for something he hadn't done. But then he realised he wasn't lying, he just wasn't telling the whole truth. Did that matter? He decided that it didn't, so he just kept quiet and accepted Stick's pat-on-the-back.

When he got back home, Red thought about it and thought about it. Did it matter that he hadn't told the whole truth?

He thought about it so much that his head began to hurt, so he stopped thinking about it and got ready for bed.

He curled-up in his cosy bed of moss and leaves and slowly fell fast asleep.

Chapter 7

Operation Grey-Away

As the days of winter went by, the red squirrels ate well and became big and strong. The grey squirrels became desperate for food as their stores disappeared. Spring arrived and soon it was time for 'Operation Grey-Away'.

Whiskers whistled signals around the forest and the red squirrels took-up their positions. They were all bright-eyed and bushy-tailed and they all knew what they had to do.

The pine martens heard the whistling and knew something was happening, so PM told One Fang to get everyone into their positions at the end of the clearing.

All the red squirrels and all the pine martens were ready and alert. The greys sniffed-out the food that had been scattered in the clearing and they all came there to eat it. First one, then two, then more and more. Eventually there were hundreds of them!

The reds waited as the greys ate. They waited and waited but the greys didn't follow the trail of food down the clearing.

"What are we going to do?" whispered Whiskers, as he sat waiting next to Red.

Red twiddled the long, red hairs at the ends of his long, red ears. They'd grown back even longer than before and his red fur coat was even more magnificent now. Whiskers twiddled his whiskers which had grown back into a fabulous moustache like he used to have. They were both thinking.

After a while, Red broke the silence and whispered, "I'm going to show them my nuts!" Whiskers looked surprised, so Red showed him the pine nuts he'd brought to nibble on if they felt peckish.

"Oh, pine nuts!" whispered Whiskers and they both giggled quietly.

Whiskers whistled to the others about the change of plan so that they all knew what was happening. Red continued to watch the greys carefully.

When the timing was right and all the greys had their heads down sniffing-out the food, Red started to crawl out from his hiding place.

"Psst!" Red stopped and looked around but couldn't see anybody. He started crawling again. "Psst!" Red stopped again.

"I'm going to show them my nuts!"

"Red! It is I!" Red knew who was whispering. He'd recognise that voice anywhere.

"Where are you?" he whispered back, as he looked around.

"By the rock."

Red looked over to the rock in the clearing and there was Her Ladyship, looking as fabulous as ever with a huge headband full of pine cones and nuts and acorns.

"Why are you here?" he whispered.

"Shhh! Get over here!" she insisted in a low voice.

He did as she commanded. Her Ladyship must be obeyed at all times. He crawled towards the rock. It was very near to where the greys were feasting.

As Red approached her, she beckoned him to stand close by her side. He touched her and he felt tingles up and down his back, his tail bushed-out and he felt slightly dizzy. He'd never been this close to Her Ladyship before. He'd never touched her before. He thought he was going to faint and he grabbed the rock to steady himself.

"Pull yourself together, Red!" she commanded. "What is wrong with you? Oh never mind. Do not talk, just listen."

She paused. Then with a raised eyebrow, a smile and a sideways glance she asked, "Are you really going to show them your nuts?"

"Yes. These." He held-out his paws full of pine nuts and showed them to her.

"Oh. Your pine nuts." Her Ladyship paused and then said, "I have brought delicious food to tempt them."

She gestured towards her headband with her beautiful nails that were longer and shinier than ever before. She looked stunning. Red began to swoon again but took a deep breath and listened carefully.

"You climb up onto the rock," she instructed quickly. "Show them your pine nuts. I will leap out. They will see all the food. We will start running down the clearing. They will follow us. Have you got it?"

"Yes, ma'am." Red saluted Her Ladyship then bowed. As he stood upright, she kissed him on the cheek.

"For good luck, Red. Be careful," she said.

"I have brought delicious food to tempt them."

He was stunned but instantly he kissed her back on the cheek. "You be careful too, ma'am." They looked into each other's eyes and time seemed to stand still.

Red swiftly climbed to the top of the rock, he stood up and raised his front paws full of pine nuts high into the air.

"Over here!" he shouted, as he waved his paws full of nuts.

The grey squirrels instantly looked up and they saw the delicious pine nuts. They wanted them. Then Her Ladyship jumped-out from behind the rock and they saw her headband full of nuts and delicious things to eat. They wanted them too. They started to run towards them.

"Over here!"

Red leapt down from the rock and he and Her Ladyship both started running down the clearing. He was a fast runner; she leapt high in the air and was able to keep-up with him. They were faster than the greys who were bigger and less agile.

On and on they ran and all the red squirrels were cheering them on. They ran down the clearing and they saw the pine martens who'd gathered there. Her Ladyship squealed with fright but she was brave and kept on running with Red.

PM jumped-out and reared-up like a bear. This was his signal for the pine martens to start chasing the greys. Red grabbed Her Ladyship's paw and they darted sideways to hide behind a tree. The greys shot past them with the pine martens close behind.

On and on they ran. Red looked-out from behind the tree and watched them all as they got smaller and smaller in the distance. Eventually he couldn't see them.

It had worked! 'Operation Grey-Away' was a total success!

Red was exhausted and he lay down for a quick nap. Her Ladyship flopped down beside him and rested her head on his chest for a pillow.

Soon they fell into a deep sleep. They slept and slept and slept.

Chapter 8

Happily Ever After?

"Here you are!" exclaimed Whiskers. "I've been looking all over for you!"

Red opened one eye and saw Whiskers peering down at him.

"Her Ladyship said I might find you here."

"How did she know…?" began Red, and then he remembered everything. The kisses, the chase, the long sleep. He looked around for her but she'd gone. "Oh yes. Yes. I remember."

"You're a hero, Red! Your plan worked! All the greys have gone! Her Ladyship wishes to see you. You're a hero! You're a hero!"

"Here you are!" exclaimed Whiskers.

Whiskers was very excited. He was leaping around and twiddling his whiskers, thinking of all the celebrations that had been planned and all the happy days ahead.

"Her Ladyship wishes to see me?" Red asked.

"Yes. Right away. She commands it."

"Well if the lady commands it, then she must be obeyed!" smiled Red, and he jumped to his feet. "Let's go!" he said, and they set-off back up the clearing.

As they got to 'Her Ladyship's Residence', they saw a lot of activity but it wasn't preparations for celebrations. The red squirrels were darting here, there and everywhere. They were all in a panic.

"Oh Red! Red! I thought you were dead!"

"Oh my goodness," exclaimed Red with a worried look. "I do hope Her Ladyship is all right. You wait here, Whiskers, and guard the entrance. I'll go in and find out what's wrong."

Whiskers nodded and stood to attention. He was good at guarding entrances. Red went in.

"Who is there?" demanded Her Ladyship.

"It's Red, ma'am."

She rushed towards him and gave him a huge hug. "Oh Red! Red! I thought you were dead!" she exclaimed. "I thought you had been eaten alive." Her eyes filled with tears and she kissed him over and over on both cheeks.

"No, I'm fine, ma'am." Red said with surprise. He wasn't expecting this! "Why did you think that?"

"Have you not heard?"

"Heard what?" Red asked with a puzzled look.

"The pine martens have been eating the greys."

"What? No, that can't be true. PM said they would chase them out of the forest. That's all."

"It is true. They have been eating them. And then they will come after us!" moaned Her Ladyship. She was very upset and worried for everyone's safety.

Red could see she needed reassurance. "Leave this to me," he said calmly.

"What are you going to do?"

"I'm going to see PM."

"No! No! Do not go, Red. If anything happens to you I think I will die."

Her Ladyship wasn't being hysterical; she wasn't being over-dramatic; she genuinely thought she would die.

Red gently placed his front paw on her cheek. He looked straight into her tearful eyes.

"PM is my friend," he said. "He will not eat me. I will be fine. He would not go back on his word. I need to find out if this is true." He then kissed her on her forehead. He kissed her on her cheek. He kissed her on her paws.

She held her face up for Red to kiss her on her lips, but he resisted. She was Her Ladyship and she was in distress. He would not take advantage of her in her hour of need. He bowed and left.

Red rushed past Whiskers and called-out, "Guard her well, Whiskers!"

"I will!" responded Whiskers with a salute.

Red was on a mission. He quickly got to the part of the forest where the pine martens lived and he could feel they were watching him.

He stood tall and called-out, "PM! It's Red! I need to speak with you! It's urgent!"

Silence. He couldn't hear a sound but he could feel he wasn't alone.

He called again, "PM! It's Red! I need to speak with you urgently!"

The silence continued. Red saw dark shadows moving in the trees. He knew the pine martens were there.

"PM! It's Red! Can I speak with you urgently? PLEASE!"

"That's the magic word, Red. Hi there! What's all the fuss about?"

PM jumped down from a tree and walked up to Red. One Fang leapt down to be beside his boss.

It was dark in this part of the forest. Everything was in shadows but as the spring sunshine broke through the canopy of trees, Red could see their faces. PM and One Fang had blood smeared on their chins and on their cream bibs.

Red held-out his paw to shake PM's.

Red gasped. Blood! Was it true?
Were they eating the greys? He decided he
mustn't jump to conclusions. He twiddled
his ear hairs and relaxed his stance.

"Hello PM," he said nervously but with
confidence. "Hello One Fang. I just want to
thank you, PM, for all the help you gave us.
Operation Grey-Away was a great success.
Thank you very much. You are a true
friend."

Red held-out his paw to shake PM's.
PM raised his paw but it was to scratch his
head. "Is that why you need to speak to me
urgently?" PM asked slowly.

"Well…yes," stammered Red. "I was
taught to say 'thank you' whenever
somebody does you a good deed. And you
did us all a really good deed, PM. The greys
were chased away and we've got our forest
back. Thank you!"

PM glanced at One Fang. One Fang glanced back at PM. They didn't say a word. Red continued to speak.

"I see you both have blood on your faces. Did you cut yourselves? Did you get hurt in the chase? Did the greys fight back and injure you? Here, let me have a look."

Red moved closer to get a better look but PM and One Fang both took a step backwards.

"No. No. We're OK, Red. Probably war wounds. They'll heal." PM muttered, and he held up his paw to cover his face.

"Are you sure you're not injured?" asked Red.

"Yeah, I'm fine," said PM.

"I'd hate to think my friend had got hurt helping me," continued Red.

"Friend?" PM asked with a puzzled look.

"Yes. Friend. I trust you, PM, and you've helped me twice now. First you showed me where the greys had hidden our food. Then you helped chase them away. You are a true friend. I will treasure our friendship for ever."

PM looked straight at Red. Red looked straight back at him. Again Red offered his paw to shake PM's. PM looked at it, then looked at One Fang, then looked back at Red's paw. He took a deep breath and said, "Come with me, Red. There's somethin' I want yer to see."

Red's mind was filled with questions. Could this be a trap? Could this be the end? Was he going to be eaten by PM? Should he run away? Would that solve anything or just make things worse? Should he cry for help? Would anybody hear? Would anybody come?

All these questions flashed through Red's mind. He took a deep breath and calmly said, "Of course, PM. Lead the way."

Red followed PM deep into the forest. It got darker and cooler and damper. Red began to shiver but he wasn't cold - he was nervous and a little bit frightened.

Eventually, they got to a place where there were trees with hollows and there were burrows where animals had lived. He could hear noises. They were high-pitched screams. Oh no! Was he going to be tortured? PM started to chuckle. Oh no! Was PM looking forward to watching him die?

Red felt dizzy and he stumbled. As he lay flat on the ground, he looked up and then he saw them.

"Daddy's home! Daddy's home!" cried two baby pine martens. They'd popped their heads out of one of the hollows in a huge pine tree and were squealing with delight as they watched PM approaching.

"Treats, daddy! Treats! Hungry, daddy! Hungry! Eat treats! Eat treats!" they squeaked.

"Hi there, kits! Come on out! Come and meet Red. He's…erm…he's…erm… he's my friend."

They scampered to the ground and got tangled-up in their excitement! They ran to their daddy. They hugged his legs and they hugged his neck. They clung on to him and

The other kit was a little bit shy.

climbed up onto his back. They were laughing and screaming with delight as he walked around with them on his back.

PM loved his kids and they loved him. They jumped off him and ran to Red. One of them jumped onto his back and nearly squashed him.

Red laughed! He'd been a daddy many times before but he'd never played with his little ones. This was fun!

The other kit was a little bit shy. It was standing and watching them play but didn't join in the fun.

"She ain't seen a red squirrel before," explained PM. "She don't know what to make of yer."

"Don't be scared. Come and play!" Red said with a smile as he held out his paw.

"I call this one Cheeky Chops."

She smiled and shuffled a little bit closer. The other kit jumped off Red's back, ran over to PM and stood there licking his lips.

"I call this one Cheeky Chops. He's always after food, ain't yer?" said PM, as he looked down lovingly.

PM tossed some food over by the pine tree and the kits scampered-off to find it. His huge smile gradually disappeared and then he turned to look at Red. He spoke with a serious voice.

"I'm their daddy. Their mummy is dead. You've seen One Fang's scar and missin' eye?" Red nodded. "Well, he was lucky. A fox trap nearly got 'im but he was able to pull himself free."

PM paused then continued. "The kits' mummy wasn't so lucky. She couldn't escape. She died a long, slow death in that trap."

PM looked away and Red could see a tear fall onto his cream bib. He flicked it away and stood watching the kits playing rough-and-tumble with each other.

Eventually, PM turned back and looked at Red again. "They need to eat. I need to eat. You need to eat. We all need to eat," he said.

Red nodded. He remembered how hungry he had been in the winter before he met PM. He remembered how his hair was falling out, how skinny he was and how he was just about to give up as he lay down on the log. Of course he needs to eat. Of course the pine martens need to eat too.

"Yer know pine martens eat squirrels, don't yer?" PM continued.

Red nodded.

"Well, we ate some greys…"

"But you said you would chase them away!" shouted Red. "You said you'd chase them and they'd be so frightened that they'd run far away from the forest! That's what you said. You didn't say you'd eat them!"

Red was very upset and annoyed with PM. He was angry.

"True," replied PM calmly. "But I didn't say we wouldn't eat 'em, did I? What I told you was the truth, it just wasn't the whole truth."

Red was about to argue with PM but suddenly he remembered what had happened when he told Stick about the plan to chase the greys away. He'd told him the plan and Stick had thought it was Red's idea. Red didn't say it was and he didn't say it wasn't. He hadn't told Stick the whole truth.

Red took a deep breath and shook his head. He looked down in shame. He was sad and slowly he said, "I'm sorry, PM. I thought you'd lied to me and you hadn't. I'm sorry I got angry. I know you eat squirrels because my mummy told me that. She told me over and over again. Yes of course you have to eat <u>and</u> you have your kits to feed too. I'm sorry."

"That's OK, Red. That's OK," said PM with a gentle voice.

"Can we still be friends?" Red asked.

"Haha! Sure we can!"

"And can we all live together in the forest?"

"Yes! It's not my forest, it's not your forest, it's everybody's forest!"

"And will you promise not to eat the red squirrels?"

"What's the magic word?"

"Please?"

"Yeah! I promise not to eat yer! Yer faster than us anyway and yer get high up in the trees onto them thin branches where we can't get."

"Yes! We'll run up high and you won't catch us! Deal?" Red asked, with his paw outstretched.

"Yeah! Let's shake on it!"

"Yeah! Let's shake on it!"

Red stretched up onto his tiptoes to reach up to PM's paw. They both smiled big smiles and then they shook paws. PM's paw was much bigger than Red's and he could have crushed it if he'd tried. But he didn't.

They shook paws and looked straight into each other's eyes with big smiles on their faces. They were friends and they'd made a deal!

* * * * * * *

So Red and PM made a deal and they shook paws, but did PM keep his promise? Did they all live happily ever after?

That's for them to know and for you to find out…

INFORMATION

'The Squirrel' is a story for children that is fiction based on fact. The red squirrel is an endangered species in the UK and the grey squirrel threatens its survival, however the pine marten is coming to its rescue.

This section is for more advanced readers and for adults. It gives information about red squirrels and pine martens. It also gives information about some of the charities that are working to bring back these native animals from the brink of extinction. All profits from sales of this book are donated to these charities to help them continue their hard work.

The meanings of words that children may not know or understand are given at the end of this section. These words will help them to increase their vocabulary.

What 'The Squirrel' teaches children

'The Squirrel' is the first of nine Lunn Learning books that educate children about nature, wildlife and conservation through stories. It is a work of fiction based on fact so that children learn about the appearance, habitat, diet and behaviour of red squirrels and pine martens as they read an exciting and entertaining story.

Red Squirrels have 'Super-Skills' of physical agility, memory, intelligence, problem-solving and determination and these are demonstrated by Red and his friends throughout the story.

In addition, human qualities, emotions, ethics and morals are presented in an anthropomorphic way through the story's characters. Children read about friendship, teamwork, leadership, affection & love, respect & manners as the red squirrels interact with each other. Trust, bravery, deception and honesty are interwoven in the interplay between the pine martens and the main character, Red.

THE RED SQUIRREL 'sciurus vulgaris'

What is it?

The red squirrel is a native British mammal. It is
a member of the rodent family, which includes
mice, rats, beavers, guinea pigs and hamsters.

What does it look like?

The red squirrel is about 20cm long. It usually
has bright reddish-brown fur but it can have
colours ranging from ginger to dark brown; its
underside is creamy-white. It has large ear tufts
and a long, fluffy tail. Its bushy tail is as long as

its body and it helps the squirrel to balance and steer when jumping from tree to tree and running along branches. Its tail is also used for communication and it helps the squirrel to keep warm while it sleeps.

Where do they live?

Red squirrels are arboreal and are found in evergreen coniferous forests and deciduous broadleaf woodlands. They make a drey out of twigs in a branch-fork, forming a domed structure which is lined with moss, leaves, grass and bark. They also use tree hollows and woodpecker holes for their drey.

What do they eat?

Red squirrels are granivore-herbivores. They gnaw the scales off pine cones to get at the seeds inside and then discard the cores.

They mostly eat the seeds of trees but their diet can vary greatly throughout the year to include fungi, nuts (especially hazelnuts), berries and young shoots. Excess food is put into caches – either buried in the ground or in nooks and holes in trees - and eaten when food is scarce.

Red squirrels love hazelnuts but cannot digest acorns, so they are more likely to live in mixed woodland that contains hazel rather than oak trees.

Why are they important?

Red squirrels have been in the UK for over 10,000 years and they are part of the countryside and our natural heritage. They are vital for woodland health and regeneration. They like to eat pine seeds and also eat the seeds of larch and spruce trees. In doing this, they help to disperse the seeds, which plays a vital role in the reforestation process of forests.

Why are they endangered?

The number of red squirrels in the UK drastically reduced after grey squirrels were brought into the UK from North America in the 1870s. Also, their woodland habitat has been broken-up and even destroyed in places.

The non-native grey squirrels decrease the red squirrel population mainly due to disease. The grey squirrels carry the squirrelpox virus which does not appear to affect their own health but it is fatal to red squirrels. Once it is in a population of squirrels, the virus spreads very quickly and woodlands can quickly lose all their red squirrels.

Grey squirrels are larger and more robust than the reds and they are better at competing for food. Also, they can digest nuts with high tannin content such as acorns, whereas red squirrels cannot digest them easily. This limits the food that is available for red squirrels and forces them to live elsewhere in areas where it is more difficult for them to survive.

Over time, grey squirrels replace red squirrels. This is why red squirrels are rare and it is very difficult to see one even in wild countryside.

What is being done to protect them?

To preserve red squirrels, they must be kept apart from grey squirrels as the two species cannot live together long-term.

The Wildlife Trusts has been at the forefront of efforts to save red squirrels for decades. It works on habitat management to help red squirrels and it targets control of grey squirrels in areas where red squirrels are at risk of extinction.

Red Squirrels United is led by The Wildlife Trusts. It is a partnership of academics, practitioners and volunteers, working together on a programme of red squirrel conservation. It was launched in 2015 and it focusses on conserving red squirrel populations in specific areas in Northern Ireland, Northern England and Wales.

The **Red Squirrel Survival Trust** conserves and protects the red squirrel in the UK by doing three main things: it is working to keep reds and greys apart, it is establishing new red colonies across the UK, and it is protecting the biodiversity of Britain's native woodlands to secure the environment in which red squirrels can thrive.

British Red Squirrel is a group of volunteers from across the UK who are passionate about red squirrel conservation and grey control. It works alongside other organisations to raise awareness of the squirrel situation in the British Isles and to help the general public become involved.

Woodland Trust is working with partners in projects across Britain to develop long-term conservation strategies that deter greys and encourage reds. They are establishing areas around red squirrel strongholds that control grey squirrels, and helping landowners to improve habitats for squirrels. They are also planting trees to connect areas of woodland which increases the habitats for red squirrels and many other woodland species.

People's Trust for Endangered Species is helping to return red squirrels to woodlands in the north-west Highlands of Scotland. Sites are carefully chosen in areas where the red squirrels would be safe from grey squirrels. Then, red squirrels are taken from other parts of Scotland where they are doing well and translocated to new woodland homes in the Highlands.

Did you know?

Red squirrels can swim.

They do not hibernate so they store food in the ground in the autumn to eat over the wintertime.

They can climb down trees head first because they are able to rotate their ankle joints backwards.

They can be left-handed and right-handed. The nibble marks on the pine cones they discard have been studied and the direction of the gnawing tracks made by their lower incisors shows which paw the squirrel used to hold the cone.

The red squirrel's big, bushy tail is as long as its body and is used to keep it warm as it sleeps.

An adult red squirrel weighs about 330g which is lighter than a football.

The collective noun for squirrels is a **scurry**.

THE PINE MARTEN 'martes martes'

What is it?

The pine marten is a native British mammal and a member of the mustelid family which includes weasels, otters and badgers.

What does it look like?

The pine marten is the size of a small domestic cat. It has rich, thick, shiny chocolate-brown fur and a creamy-yellow chest 'bib'. It has a pointed face and small, rounded, highly sensitive ears which are tipped with yellow, and it has sharp teeth. It has a long bushy tail that it uses to help it balance in trees. It is the only mustelid that has semi-retractable claws that enable it to climb trees as well as run along the ground.

Where do they live?

Pine martens live in woodland habitats and prefer well-wooded areas with plenty of cover. Their dens are often in hollow trees or the roots of fallen Scots Pine trees, which is probably why they are called 'Pine Martens'. They are mostly nocturnal but are frequently active during the day especially in the summer months.

What do they eat?

Pine martens are omnivores and have a varied diet. They will eat small animals such as birds, voles, rabbits and squirrels, and they eat carrion, eggs, fungi, fruit and berries. Pine martens are predators. They mostly hunt on the ground, although they are superb climbers and can climb trees quickly and easily.

Why are they important?

The pine marten is part of our natural heritage. It plays an integral role in a healthy, balanced woodland ecosystem and it can be an important predator of pest species such as grey squirrels.

They are an important part of a healthy, balanced woodland ecosystem because they help to control prey populations. Research suggests that the presence of pine martens can be beneficial for the endangered red squirrel. This is because predation by pine martens has been found to naturally decrease the population of the grey squirrels which spread disease to the red squirrels and outcompete them for food.

Pine martens prey on grey squirrels more successfully than on red squirrels because the greys are slower and spend more time on the ground than reds, making them a much easier target.

Why are they endangered?

Pine martens were once widespread throughout Britain but this decreased drastically during the 19th century as a result of persecution and deforestation. By the early 20th century, the pine marten had become extinct across most of Britain and only survived in the Scottish Highlands and tiny areas of Wales and northern England.

The pine marten is critically endangered in England and Wales. It is a protected species and their numbers are on the increase, but dangers are still present because much of its woodland habitat has been lost. This is the biggest danger because pine martens rely on woodland with good tree cover in order to survive.

Pine martens predate game birds so they are illegally killed by humans to secure the bird populations for game hunting. They also get caught in traps meant for other animals such as foxes.

What is being done to protect them?

The pine marten receives full protection under the Wildlife and Countryside Act 1981. Pine marten populations began to recover in Scotland when laws to protect them were introduced. They are still absent from most of England and Wales, however they have begun to spread from Scotland and recolonise Northumberland, Cumbria, Yorkshire and Shropshire.

The **Vincent Wildlife Trust** has set-up a **Pine Marten Recovery Project** which aims to restore pine marten populations to England and Wales by translocation from Scotland.

The Wildlife Trusts together with the Vincent Wildlife Trust and the Forestry Commission has plans to bring a small population down from Scotland to reintroduce the pine marten to the Forest of Dean and lower Wye Valley. The aim is for the population to link up with a recently established Welsh pine marten population. These two populations will strengthen each other and greatly increase the chances of their survival across England and Wales.

Woodland Trust is supporting a programme to restore pine martens in England and Wales.

Did you know?

Pine martens are strong swimmers.

The pine marten is sometimes also known as the marten cat, sweetmart or sweet marten, perhaps because it likes to eat sweet treats.

They mark their territories with scats deposited in places where they will be found by other pine martens.

They can leap a horizontal distance of up to four metres, and are able to land unhurt on their feet from heights of around 20 metres – over four times the height of a double-decker bus!

Source: People's Trust for Endangered Species

The collective noun for pine martens is a **richness**.

CHARITIES

 Red Squirrels United

www.redsquirrelsunited.org.uk

 Red Squirrel Survival Trust

www.rsst.org.uk

 British Red Squirrel

www.britishredsquirrel.org

People's Trust for Endangered Species

www.ptes.org

Vincent Wildlife Trust

www.vwt.org.uk

 Pine Marten Recovery Project

www.pine-marten-recovery-project.org.uk

 The Wildlife Trusts

www.wildlifetrusts.org

 Woodland Trust

www.woodlandtrust.org.uk

"Red squirrels are officially classed* as 'near threatened' in England, Wales and Northern Ireland."   (Woodland Trust 2019)

*Classified by IUCN

"Time is really running out to save the red squirrels. Unfortunately, without conservation management, red squirrels could become extinct in England in approximately 10 years. To preserve red squirrels, they must be kept apart from grey squirrels as the two species cannot live together long term."

(The Wildlife Trusts 2019)

"Research has suggested the presence of pine martens can be beneficial for the endangered red squirrel. This is because predation by martens has been found to suppress the population of non-native grey squirrels, which outcompete and spread disease to the native reds."

(Woodland Trust 2019)

"Whilst the pine marten population in Scotland is recovering and expanding, the population in England and Wales has shown no sign of recovery and the likely outcome is extinction."

(Vincent Wildlife Trust 2019)

SPECIAL WORDS

Academic: person who works in education

Annually: occurring once every year

Anthropomorphic: having human characteristics

Anus: the hole in an animal's bottom

Arboreal: lives in trees

Bark: tough outer layer of trunks, branches and twigs of trees and woody shrubs

Beneficial: favourable or advantageous

Biodiversity: the variety of plant and animal life in a particular habitat

Broadleaf tree: tree with flat leaves and produces seeds inside fruits

Cache: a hidden store

Canine teeth: long, sharp, pointed, fang-like teeth

Carnivore: animal that feeds on flesh

Carrion: decaying flesh of dead animals

Charities: organisations that raise money and provide help for those in need

Collective noun: word for a group of the same things

Communication: exchange of information

Coniferous: of the conifer tree with needle-like leaves and seeds in woody cones

Conservation: preservation and restoration of the natural environment and wildlife

Countryside: the land and scenery of a rural area

Critically endangered: an extremely high risk of extinction in the wild, as classed by the IUCN

Decade: period of ten years

Deciduous: tree or shrub that sheds its leaves annually

Decompose: decay and become rotten

Deforestation: clearing forests and cutting-down trees

Deter: discourage from doing something

Diet: the kinds of food that an animal eats

Digest: break-down food in the stomach or intestines

Discard: get rid of something and throw it away

Disease: a disorder of structure or function in an organism

Disperse: distribute in different directions over a wide area

Donated: given for a good cause

Drey: squirrel's nest

Ecosystem: community of living things and their surroundings

Edible: can be eaten as food

Encourage: give support and hope

Endangered: at risk or in danger of becoming extinct

Environment: the surroundings in which an animal lives; the natural world affected by human activity

Evergreen: a plant that has green leaves throughout the year

Excess: more than is needed

Extinct: no longer existing; having no living members

Extinction: the state of being extinct

Fatal: causing death or leading to disaster

Fauna: animals of a particular region or habitat

Fiction: describing imaginary events

Flora: plants of a particular region or habitat

Forest: a large area covered with trees and undergrowth

Fungi: organisms which include mushrooms, toadstools, yeasts and moulds

Game bird: bird shot for sport or food

Gene: unit of information that determines a characteristic of an individual

Gnaw: bite or nibble for a long time

Granivore-herbivore: animal that primarily eats seeds from plants and trees

Habitat: natural home where particular species live

Herbivore: animal that feeds on plants

Hibernate: spend the winter sleeping

Incisors: front teeth in mammals used to cut food

Inhabitant: animal that lives in a place

Inherited: received from past generations

Inhibit: hinder or prevent something

Integral: fundamental and necessary

Intestines: tubes joining the stomach to the anus

Invasion: an unwelcome presence of large numbers of living things that spread-out and may attack

IUCN: International Union for Conservation of Nature

Kit: young pine marten (short for 'kitten')

Mammal: warm-blooded animal with a backbone

Moss: small, green, low-growing plant that forms layers or rounded lumps

Mould: furry growth that decomposes dead organic matter

Mushroom: a type of fungus that is usually shaped like an umbrella and may be edible

Mustelid: family of mammals including pine martens, weasels, otters, badgers, stoats, polecats, mink, the wolverine

Native: occurring naturally in a place

Natural heritage: flora, fauna, ecosystems and geological structures inherited from past generations

Near threatened: a species that may be considered threatened with extinction in the near future, as classed by the IUCN

Nocturnal: active at night

Nook: corner or hollow

Nutrient: substance that provides essential food for life and growth

Omnivore: animal that feeds on plants and animals

Organic: relating to or made from living matter

Organism: an individual life-form

Outcompete: displace another species in the competition for space, food or other things

Parasite: an organism that lives on or inside another organism from which it gets nutrients

Persecution: being hunted by humans

Pest species: destructive animal that attacks crops or other animals

Poisonous: cause extreme harm or death when introduced into a living organism

Population: all the inhabitants of a particular place

Practitioner: person who puts theory into practice

Predation: the hunting of an animal by others

Predator: animal that hunts and kills other animals for food

Preservation: activity aimed at maintaining and prolonging life

Prey: an animal that is hunted and killed by another animal for food

Promise: agreement to do a particular thing or that something will definitely happen

Protect: keep safe from harm or injury

Recolonise: live in regions again

Reforestation: natural or intentional restocking of existing forests and woodlands

Regeneration: bringing new and more rigorous life

Research: investigation to find-out facts and new information

Restoration: activity aimed at returning something to its original state

Robust: strong and healthy

Rodent: mammal that gnaws with growing incisors and has no canine teeth

Rural: not in a town or city

Scarce: not enough for what is needed

Scats: animal faeces (droppings)

Semi-retractable claws: claws that can be pulled-back slightly into the paws

Species: a group of living organisms consisting of similar individuals capable of exchanging genes

Squirrelpox: fatal disease for UK red squirrels. The virus is often carried by grey squirrels which rarely die from the disease.

Starvation: suffering or death caused by lack of food

Stash: store safely in a secret place

Stomach: tummy

Stronghold: a place that is protected against attack

Suppress: hinder or prevent something

Survival: the ability to keep living or existing

Tannin: bitter-tasting organic substance

Territory: area occupied by an animal which it defends against other animals of the same species

Theory: idea to explain something

Threatened: put at risk or put in danger

Toadstool: a mushroom-like fungus that may often be poisonous

Translocate: move from one place to another

Underside: chest and tummy of an animal

Virus: a very tiny particle which is able to multiply within the cells of an organism causing an infection or disease

Vital: essential and necessary

Vocabulary: words used in a particular language

Volunteer: person who freely offers to do something

Wildlife: native flora and fauna of a region which live freely in the natural environment

Woodland: land covered with trees

Yeast: tiny fungus that is often used in making bread, beer, wine and spirits